Easi-Bild®
BUILD-IT-YOURSELF®
CATALOG

Patterns
Home Improvement Books
Educational Film Strips

REVISED EDITION

Published by
DIRECTIONS SIMPLIFIED, INC.

Division of
EASI-BILD PATTERN CO., INC.
Briarcliff Manor, NY 10510

TABLE OF CONTENTS

Easi-Bild® BOOK ORDER FORM

PLEASE SEND THE FOLLOWING:

PRICES SUBJECT TO CHANGE WITHOUT NOTICE

603
How to Build a Dormer

Everyone who needs more living or storage space should read this book. It explains how to install stairs, raise one half or both sides of the roof to gain headroom. Air conditioning permits turning attic space into one or more extra bedrooms, a complete apartment. 82pp., 114 illus.

TO CREATE MORE LIVING SPACE

665
How to Modernize an Attic

Those who need more living space or extra income should read this book. It explains how to transform an attic into prime living space. Every step explained and illustrated. Learn how to install a skylight, install framing for a louver or air conditioning unit, build a stairway, partitions and apply prefinished paneling like a pro. Even explains construction of a free standing storage wall. 82pp., 86 illus.

608
How to Modernize
a Kitchen

Read how to economically modernize
a kitchen building base and wall
cabinets to fit space available. Learn
how to install floor tile, indirect
lighting, etc. Every step clearly illustrated. 82pp., 118 illus.

READ - LEARN - SAVE BIG MONEY

658
How to Build Kitchen
Cabinets, Room Dividers,
Cabinet Furniture

The pole type base and wall cabinet
furniture built according to directions
outlined in this book, cuts kitchen
modernization costs to the bone.
Every step illustrated. Directions explain how to build to any width, depth
and height space allows. Aluminum
extrusions, plus prefinished hardwood paneling, encourages amateurs
to make like pros. 98pp., 134 illus.

609
How to Build an Addition

If your family needs more living space, or needs an in-law apartment with a separate entrance, this book explains every step. Tells how to build a 12 x 16 or 16 x 20 addition with a gable or shed roof. The book for those who need more house or rental income. 96pp., 110 illus.

CREATE CAPITAL GAINS

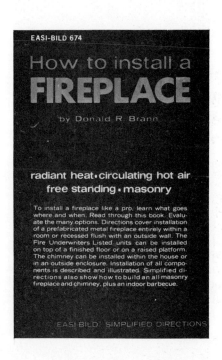

674
How to Install a Fireplace

Every step of installation is clearly illustrated. Directions explain how to install a prefabricated chimney on outside or through the floors. This book helps make a dream come true at a much lower cost than anyone expects. 242pp., 354 illus.

615
How to Modernize
a Basement

If you need a recreation room, an extra bedroom, even rental income, this book explains all. With solvent singles and working couples fleeing the cities, an air conditioned basement apartment has great appeal. Directions tell how to install a grade level door with stairs down, also explain how to remove a metal enclosure and build a greenhouse (#611) over outside stairs. 98pp., 135 illus.

A BASEMENT ENTRY WITH GREAT APPEAL

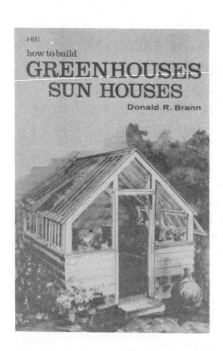

611
How to Build
Greenhouses —
Sun Houses

Everyone interested in plants and/or extra income enjoys this easy to build greenhouse. Waste heat from a basement window or entry can keep this greenhouse at proper temperature all winter. Those thinking of creating a basement apartment find a walk through greenhouse adds great appeal. It can be constructed over stairs now protected by a metal enclosure. 114pp., 110 illus.

As floor plans indicate this house offers many options. It can provide one to three bedrooms; a playroom; a truly magical kitchen, complete with a pass-through and dining counter; living room and bathroom. Directions explain how to build a basement house, one story and basement, or a two story with or without basement.

Easi-Bild® SIMPLIFIED DIRECTIONS

632
How to Build a Vacation or Retirement House

Newlyweds as well as retirees are amazed to discover this 20 x 24' house over a full basement can provide up to three bedrooms. While no larger than a two car garage, it offers a working couple or retiree a lot of house at low cost. When constructed without a basement, it contains a living room, kitchen, bathroom and bedroom. Directions explain every step of construction. 194pp., 174 illus.

TO CREATE RENTAL INCOME

Turning a garage into a living-bedroom, with or without a bathroom and kitchenette, can provide the economical and safe solution to the welfare of an aged parent. It could also become a taxpayer for a homeowner facing increased living costs. As step-by-step directions suggest, if more space is needed add to the length or width. The author assumes the reader has never attempted any major construction and explains every step.

EASI-BILD® SIMPLIFIED DIRECTIONS

684
How to Transform a Garage into Living Space

As every homeowner in need of additional income discovers, a garage can provide attractive living space for a solvent single. This book explains how to convert it into a one room apartment. A real income producer for property owners, a business of your own for everyone seeking new careers. 130pp., 139 illus.

11

763
How to Build
a Two Car Garage
and Apartment

The perfect solution and sound investment for those seeking to buy or build a home. Instead of buying and paying inflated costs, or building and being robbed blind, this book suggests reading, learning, then building a two car garage with an apartment. It provides shelter at the lowest cost in the fastest possible time, plus a long term investment. Move in and you will be smart enough to build a house like a pro. 128pp., over 200 illus.

IT'S EASY TO BECOME A LANDLORD

685
How to Rehabilitate
Abandoned Buildings

Learn how to mine gold without leaving home, regardless of your past experience. This book can turn those unemployed into rent collecting landlords with only an investment of labor. With the government giving away houses at $1.00 and lending all the funds needed for rehabilitation at 3% interest, all you need do is invest labor. 258pp., 345 illus.

12

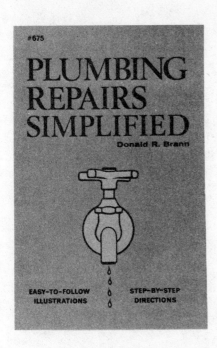

675
Plumbing Repairs Simplified

Every type of plumbing fixture repair and installation is explained and illustrated. Over 800 illustrations simplify matching needed replacement parts. These detail old fixtures as well as new. By matching picture with washer or part, getting what you need is greatly simplified. 162pp., 800 illus.

LEARN PLUMBING LIKE A PRO

682
How to Add an Extra Bathroom

Solving any problem creates new business opportunities. Learn how to install a bathroom or lavatory in a basement, attic, garage or wherever needed, then see how easily you can make the same popular improvement for others. Those who need space for extra bedrooms and bath should read Book #609. To simplify applying tile, read Book #606 How to Lay Ceramic Tile. Book #682, 162pp., 200 illus.

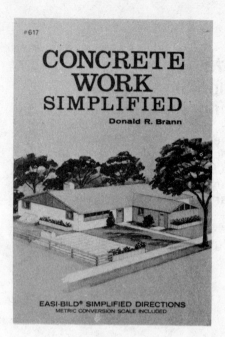

617
Concrete Work Simplified

Mixing concrete and using it like a pro is explained in detail. Besides laying walks, walls, blocks, etc., directions explain how to lay slate, flagstone, build a mixing tub, measuring box and much more. 96pp., 128 illus.

READ - LEARN - EARN

668
Bricklaying Simplified

As in all building trades, the real pro learns how to lay bricks for every end use from walls, walks, facing on houses to building two popular back-yard barbecues. Directions explain every step. 146pp., 209 illus.

14

697
Forms, Footings, Foundations and Framing

While all books explain and illustrate every step required to construct the featured project, this book contains information covering special situations, i.e., how to erect forms over a rocky or side hill site, pour concrete foundation walls, two story framing, and much, much more. The perfect gift for everyone interested in building. 162pp., 236 illus.

BUILDING TRADES EARN BIG MONEY

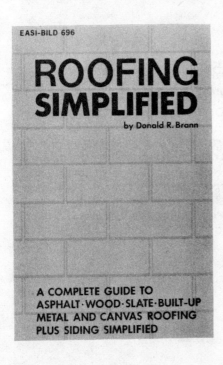

696
Roofing Simplified

Application of new roofing to making every type of roof repair is clearly explained and illustrated. To overcome the fear of working on a roof, this book explains how to make a roofer's safety harness, how to secure a safety line over the ridge. When you fasten the harness to the safety line, you can walk and work on a roof with greater ease and security than crossing many streets. 98pp., 148 illus.

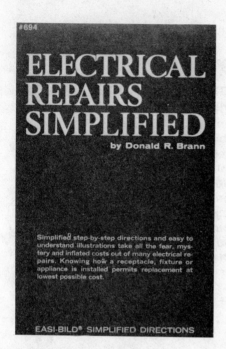

694
Electrical Repairs Simplified

Making electrical repairs is easy when you follow the step by step procedure outlined. By matching parts with pictures, you make like a pro. Every repair and installation from replacing fixtures, outlets, to running new circuits, clearly illustrated. 98pp., 185 illus.

READ - LEARN - EARN

695
How to Install Protective Alarm Devices

Learn how to protect every window and door with magnetic alarm devices for only the cost of components. Simplified directions explain and illustrate every step including installation of a telephone hookup to police headquarters. 130pp., 144 illus.

16

605
How to Apply Paneling

Prefinished hardwood plywood or hardboard paneling is easy to install when you know how. This book takes you through every step from accumulating materials to making all the intricate cuts needed to fit around pipes, stairs, doors, windows and corners out of plumb. Learn how to panel in your own home and discover how to earn money paneling walls for others. 82pp., 100 illus.

EASY TO LEARN BUILDING TRADES

606
How to Lay Ceramic Tile

No other material has the appeal, color and serviceability of ceramic tile. No quality product costs so little to install, when you do it yourself. Every step is clearly explained. Directions explain how to apply single or larger panels of ceramic tile to walls, floors, as well as counter tops. Every step explained, illustrated and simplified. This is a LEARN A TRADE book every school boy and retiree will find of interest. 82pp., 112 illus.

ONE CAR GARAGE WITH TOOL HOUSE AND WORKBENCH

ONE OR TWO BOX STALL STABLE

This book simplifies building a one car garage, complete with a workshop and garden tool storage. It also explains how to "make a dream come true," by converting a garage into a stable. Everything you need to know to build like a pro, is explained and illustrated.

680
How to Build a One Car Garage, Carport, Convert a Garage to Stable

Homeowners who need space for a workbench and garden tools, plus one car, find the 13'0" x 20'0" garage very adequate. Directions also explain how to turn a single car garage into a stable. 164pp., 181 illus.

BOARDING A HORSE CAN BE FUN

663
How to Build a Two Car Garage

Measuring 20 x 24', this code approved garage is easy to build. The book explains every step from laying concrete block to roofing, 66pp., 53 illus.

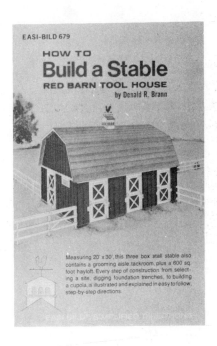

HOW TO
Build a Stable
RED BARN TOOL HOUSE
by Donald R. Brann

Measuring 20' x 30', this three box stall stable also contains a grooming aisle, tackroom, plus a 600 sq. foot hayloft. Every step of construction from selecting a site, digging foundation trenches, to building a cupola, is illustrated and explained in easy to follow, step-by-step directions

679
How to Build a Stable — Red Barn Tool House

Owning a horse was once considered beyond the means of most average income families, but along came drugs and the cost of a cure. Many parents now realize an interest in horses builds character, helps develop an individual, a loner and survivor instead of a joiner and loser. Building a three box stall stable, following directions outlined, can also put a youngster into business boarding horses for others. 178pp., 197 illus.

MAKE A DREAM COME TRUE

HOW TO BUILD
GARDEN TOOL HOUSE
CHILD'S PLAYHOUSE
by Donald R. Brann

Step-by-step directions and over 100 illustrations simplify building a tool house. Designed to accommodate gardening tools, riding mower, roller to bicycles. The house offers many features such as tool chest doors. A locked storage area provides safe, dry storage for insecticides, seeds, fertilizers, etc. Take the congestion out of your garage — build for relaxation and an economical solution to a basic storage problem. Directions also explain how to build a colorful child's playhouse and play store.

GARDEN TOOL HOUSE

COLORFUL PLAYHOUSE

EASI-BILD® SIMPLIFIED DIRECTIONS

649
How to Build a Tool House, Playhouse, Install a Sauna

We simplified construction of this 6'0" x 7'9" building for use as a garden tool house only to discover many families transformed it into a child's playhouse. More recently it's become the ideal place to install a sauna. Directions explain every step from pouring footings, foundation, framing to installation of needed equipment. 96pp., 130 illus.

19

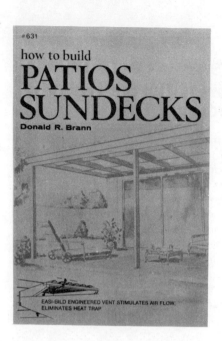

how to build
PATIOS SUNDECKS
Donald R. Brann

EASI-BILD ENGINEERED VENT STIMULATES AIR FLOW, ELIMINATES HEAT TRAP

631
How to Build Patios and Sundecks

Learn how to build a patio that doesn't create a heat trap. The Easi-Bild copyrighted roof design triggers a free flow of air. Besides simplifying construction of a patio to any size needed, the book explains how to build a raised deck, privacy partition, and much more. 82pp., 113 illus.

ENJOY MORE LIVING SPACE

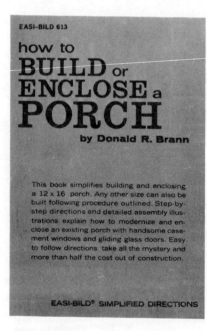

EASI-BILD 613

how to
BUILD or ENCLOSE a PORCH
by Donald R. Brann

This book simplifies building and enclosing a 12 x 16 porch. Any other size can also be built following procedure outlined. Step-by-step directions and detailed assembly illustrations explain how to modernize and enclose an existing porch with handsome casement windows and gliding glass doors. Easy to follow directions take all the mystery and more than half the cost out of construction.

EASI-BILD® SIMPLIFIED DIRECTIONS

613
How to Build or Enclose a Porch

With few exceptions most young homeowners need more living space. Those without a porch and those with one that needs enclosing find this book extremely helpful. It explains every step from building a porch, a raised deck, to enclosing an existing porch. 82pp., 112 illus.

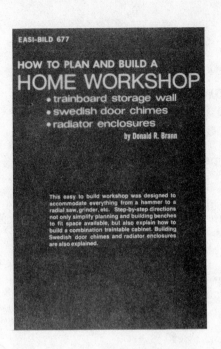

677
How to Plan and Build a Home Workshop

Step by step directions simplify building a complete power tool workshop. Benches accommodate a radial arm saw, grinder, portable electric tools, etc. 98pp., 133 illus.

TO RELIEVE TENSION

672

How to Build Workbenches and Sawhorse Tool Chest

Four different types of workbenches can be built from the simplified directions offered in this book. The 6' bench is extremely popular and can be built for resale. A folding wall bench, sawhorse tool chest, plus a table top clamp-on model offer working space for every hobby. 98pp., 90 illus., plus several full size coping saw patterns.

664
How to Construct Built-In and Sectional Bookcases

Homeowners, builders and home improvers, as well as those seeking to start a business of their own, find all the information needed to build either wall to wall or free standing; sectional units or a combination bookcase and record cabinet. Construction of a room dividing bookcase is also explained. Each is illustrated and construction simplified. 98pp., 137 illus.

SMART STORAGE IDEAS

612
How to Build Wall-to-Wall Cabinets, Stereo Installation Simplified

It's easy to build handsome floor to ceiling base and wall cabinets, plus shelving when you follow directions offered in this book. Directions not only explain how to build cabinets to fit space available, but also how to install speakers, turntable, amplifier, etc. Construction of free standing cabinets is also explained in detail. 130pp., 165 illus.

630
How to Build Sportsman's Cabinets and Racks

The two-faced, revolving gun, clothing and fishing gear storage cabinet holds just about everything from sporting gear, boots, to ammunition. Locked drawers and cabinet doors insure safe storage. Build gun racks. Show them to your friends and you'll start a business of building for resale. 98pp., 121 illus.

EASY TO BUILD CABINETS

634
How to Build Storage Units

Solve every kind of storage problem. Learn how to build wall to wall cabinets with either bi-folding, sliding or hinged doors, to free standing storage cabinets. Directions also explain how to build a cedar lined storage chest, a sewing cabinet, under the stairs storage, and an under the bed storage cabinet on wheels. 98pp., 145 illus.

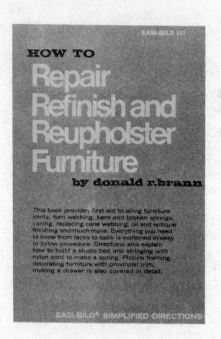

623
How to Repair, Refinish and Reupholster Furniture

Repairing furniture, recaning seats, rebuilding a damaged joint, isn't difficult, nor does it take years of training. It does require reading and doing what directions suggest. Since every family owns some piece of furniture that either needs refinishing, gluing, caning, etc., the potential for starting a business of your own is excellent. And it can be started by anyone, at any age, willing and interested. 98pp., 145 illus.

IT'S FUN WHEN YOU KNOW HOW

683
Carpeting Simplified

Read how a pro does the work in words and pictures that clearly explain every step. Directions simplify installation over every type of surface. Carpeting stairs and the use of carpeting tools is covered in detail. 146pp., 211 illus.

24

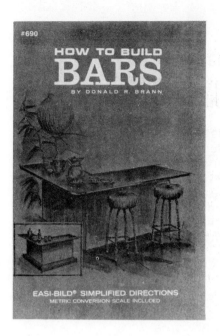

690
How to Build Bars

Easy to follow, step by step directions simplify building a straight and L shaped bar, a cabinet bar on casters, plus a handsome bookcase-TV-record cabinet bar and playroom table that offer business of your own potential. 114pp., 131 illus.

YOU TOO CAN MAKE LIKE A PRO

This book explains how to install traverse drapery track, make valance, cornice boards and draperies; frame a window, build shelves between windows, and many other decorative projects. Step-by-step directions and illustrations take all the mystery out of installing drapery track and curtain hardware.

627
How to Make Cornice Boards, Draperies, Valances, Install Traverse Track

Everything you need to know to install draperies like a pro is described in this book. Directions explain how to install traverse track and indirect lighting. Full size patterns simplify making valance boards plus a wall cabinet that can be built to fill space between windows. 66pp., 117 illus.

25

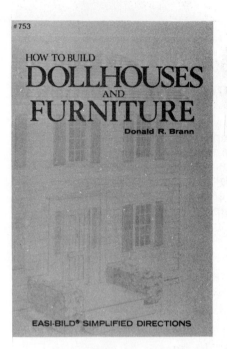

753
How to Build
Dollhouses — Furniture

This book explains how to build three different Colonial dollhouses plus fourteen pieces of furniture. It appeals to everyone at every age. Those with time will find a ready market for these handsome dollhouses. When auctioned at fund raising bazaars, each attracts top dollar. 128pp., 200 illus.

TO START A BUSINESS OF YOUR OWN

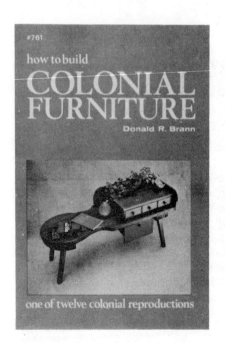

761
How to Build
Colonial Furniture

Besides providing clear, easy to follow step by step directions, this book contains full size patterns that simplify cutting curved parts. Learn how to build a Shaker Hutch Table, Cobblers Bench, Colonial Cradle, Hutch Cabinet, Under the Eaves Rope Bed and many, many other easy to sell pieces. Directions also explain how to make popular joints, oil finishing and refinishing. 258pp., 342 illus.

Building pet shelters can prove to be a richly rewarding experience. Directions simplify building a doghouse, an all weather cat entry, plus a unique catpartment that's easy to sell and profitable to rent. Easy to follow, step-by-step procedure explains how to build a duck inn, rabbit hutch, lean-to kennel, parakeet cage, and housing for guinea pigs, gerbils and hamsters.

EASI-BILD® SIMPLIFIED DIRECTIONS
METRIC CONVERSION-SCALE INCLUDED

751
How to Build
Pet Housing

Learn how to build dog and cat houses, rabbit hutches, parakeet cages, kennels and much more. Every step of construction explained and illustrated. Youngsters and retirees seeking to earn extra money learn rabbit meat is now in great demand. It can be bartered for other foods and meats by those who want to cut food costs. 178pp., 252 illus.

BOARD PETS, BUILD BIRDHOUSES

Attract friendly and beautiful birds—enjoy their color and song! Build a 16 room martin house, picturesque wren houses, a charming home for bluebirds, generous feeders.

METRIC DIMENSIONS INCLUDED

669
How to Build Birdhouses
and Bird Feeders

Every type of house and bird feeder from a 16 room martin house to a cottage for a wren is explained. Full size patterns simplify building wren houses and feeders. 66pp., 86 illus.

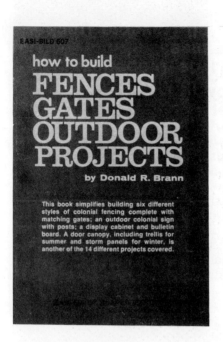

607
How to Build Fences, Gates, Outdoor Projects

Learn how to build like a pro. Full size picket patterns simplify cutting each to exact shape of those found in Colonial restorations. It's not only a fun way to build a fence, but also an easy way to start a business. Patterns simplify making six Colonial Williamsburg pickets. Directions also simplify building a Colonial sign and post, outdoor display cabinet, privacy partition and much, much more. 162pp., 200 illus.

TWO BUSINESS OF YOUR OWN BOOKS

754
How to Build Outdoor Furniture

An easy to build four passenger lawn glider, fanny fitting curved back and seat lawn chairs and settee, plus a chaise on wheels can put you into business. Place a FOR SALE sign alongside samples and watch it stop traffic. Directions also simplify building a picnic table. 128pp., 130 illus., plus full size patterns.

756
Scroll Saw Projects

This book contains 17 full size patterns that simplify building each project with professional results. Projects range from a miniature cobblers bench sewing kit, wall placques to pull toys, lawn ornaments and name plates. Ideal for the youngster seeking constructive use of spare time to retirees climbing the walls with boredom. 130pp., 144 illus.

STARTING PROJECTS FOR THE YOUNGEST

All the patterns and books offered on these pages were designed for those who can read and are willing to follow step by step directions. Donald Brann, the author of these books and designer of Easi-Bild patterns, believes everyone who can read can successfully follow every step. He believes in the two brain theory — what he can do, the reader can do.

Brann started his career at fifteen. He writes all directions without resorting to technical terms. Any step of construction that might confuse a beginner is clearly illustrated.

All full size patterns permit tracing each part on the lumber pattern specifies. Parts are cut to shape shown and joined where directions suggest. Youngsters in manual training, homeowners desirous of saving money, and retirees seeking new ways to use time constructively, find these patterns a fun and profitable way to spend time.

Adult education, trade school and rehabilitation programs quickly discover the Easi-Bild Pattern Method of Construction stimulates self-confidence, insures satisfying results.

Patterns cover every family need from outdoor furniture, building barbecues, boats, toys, bookcases, storage cabinets to building three and five bedroom houses. Everyone concerned with raising funds for a favorite charity discovers building dollhouses, lawn chaises, workbenches, rocking horses, et al, for an auction sale helps raise top dollars.

Read, learn, earn. Let these patterns and books help you turn spare time into sizable Capital Gains. Build each project to economically solve a costly problem, then do the same for others.

Easi-Bild Books are available in leading bookstores, lumber and home improvement centers. If you have difficulty getting the books or patterns from a local source, write Directions Simplified, Inc. A complete list of books and patterns is shown on pages 6,121,122. Enclose check or money order for full amount required. Please don't send cash.

FULL COLOR ADULT EDUCATION FILM STRIPS

Those interested in conducting Home Improvement Clinics will find the Easi-Bild Full Color Home Improvement Film Strips of special interest. Each 35mm film strip comes with a numbered leader's guide. The leader reads from numbered paragraphs when teaching each subject. The following Adult Education Film Strips are available:

FS600 Capital Gains Without Gambling
FS605 How to Apply Paneling
FS606 How to Lay Ceramic Tile
FS608 How to Modernize a Kitchen
FS609 How to Build an Addition
FS615 How to Modernize a Basement
FS663 How to Build a Two Car Garage
FS696 Roofing Repairs and Application Simplified

30

3 BEDROOM RANCH HOUSE NO. 501

#501 Three Bedroom Ranch House. Designed by architect Edward D. Stone for the Ladies Home Journal. This interesting ranch style house contains a large living room, play area, kitchen, bath, utility room and three bedrooms. Its construction has been designed so it can be built any additional length by extending frames any number of 4 ft. units required. Fixed glass, window and door sections are interchangeable. Build It Yourself Pattern Available.

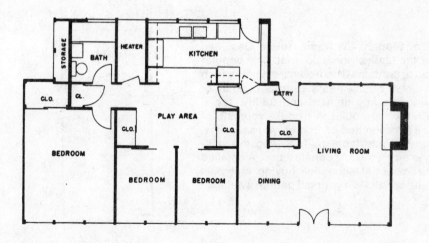

MODERN 6 ROOM HOUSE NO. 502

APPROX. 10,016 CUBIC FEET

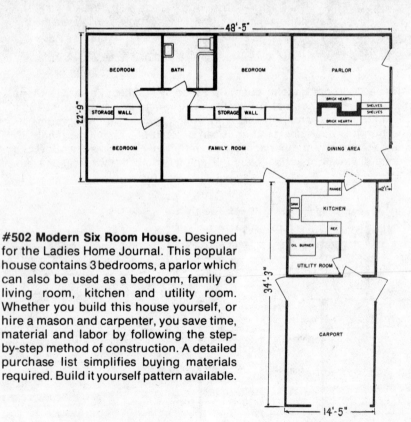

FLOOR PLAN

#502 Modern Six Room House. Designed for the Ladies Home Journal. This popular house contains 3 bedrooms, a parlor which can also be used as a bedroom, family or living room, kitchen and utility room. Whether you build this house yourself, or hire a mason and carpenter, you save time, material and labor by following the step-by-step method of construction. A detailed purchase list simplifies buying materials required. Build it yourself pattern available.

FIVE BEDROOM CAPE COD NO. 514

#514 Five Bedroom Cape Cod House. Designed by Royal Barry Wills for the Ladies Home Journal, this well styled home can accommodate a large family. Pattern method of construction takes all the mystery out of building. Complete material list, step-by-step directions and patterns for cutting rafters, gable studs, etc. Complete Build It Yourself Pattern available.

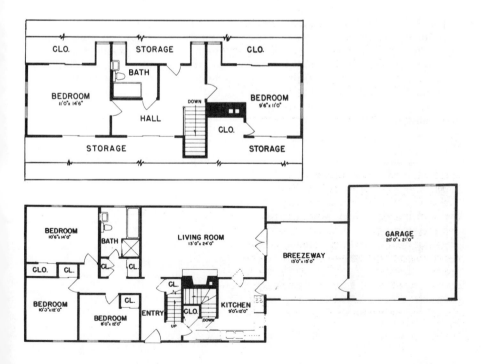

TWO BEDROOM HOUSE NO. 910

#910 Two Bedroom House. As reported in the Reader's Digest, the pattern method of construction permits unskilled persons to build this charming ranch-style house. The list of materials, assembly illustrations and step-by-step directions cover foundations, framing, sheathing, etc. The floor plan offers a large living room, two bedrooms — each with two closets, hallway with large linen closet, bathroom, kitchen, utility room, breezeway, and one car garage. Complete Build It Yourself Pattern Available.

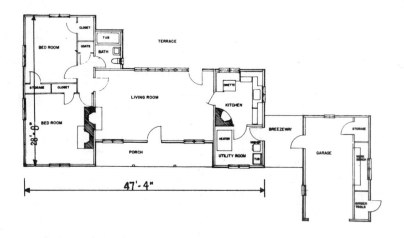

MODERN THREE BEDROOM HOUSE NO. 513

#513 Modern Three Bedroom House. Designed by the well known architectural firm of Sanders, Malsin & Reiman for the Ladies Home Journal, this modern house contains three well planned bedrooms, large living-dining room, kitchen, bathroom and multi-purpose room. Building Plans with complete material lists available.

HILLSIDE OR VALLEY HOUSE
PLANS NOS. 103H AND 103V

#103 Hillside or Valley House. Build this house on the side of a hill or on a flat piece of land. Photo shows front of both hillside and valley house. Floor plans of each show the two different room arrangements. Valley House No. 103V is built on level ground. Hillside House No. 103H is built on the side of hill with kitchen, dining and guest rooms on lower level. Plans and working drawings are available for use by builder. When ordering plans, be sure to specify whether plan No. 103V (one story) or No. 103H (side of hill) house is desired.

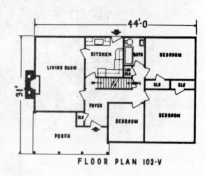

FLOOR PLAN 103-V

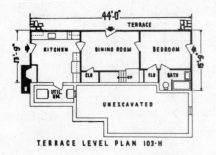

TERRACE LEVEL PLAN 103-H

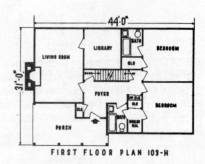

FIRST FLOOR PLAN 103-H

36

VACATION OR RETIREMENT HOUSE NO. 432

#432 Vacation or Retirement House. As floor plan indicates this house offers many options. It can provide one to three bedrooms; a playroom; a truly magical kitchen, complete with a pass-through and dining counter; living room and bathroom. Directions explain how to build a one story and basement.

Construction is also explained in Book #632.

DOWNSTAIRS ROOMS

ENTRANCE FLOOR

GUEST HOUSE NO. 84

#84 Guest House. Here's a one room house that solves the problem for an inexpensive, overnight, weekend or year 'round home.

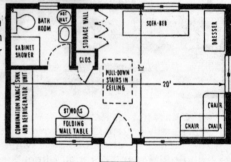

COUNTRY COTTAGE NO. 91

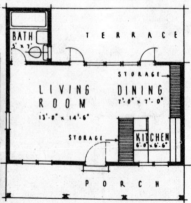

#91 Country Cottage. As the floor plan indicates, this compact cottage provides space for a kitchen, dinette, bathroom plus a combination living-bedroom. Later, two bedrooms and other rooms can be added as shown in Pattern No. 910. Step-by-step directions cover everything from laying out foundation guide lines to building house. Assembly illustrations show exact location of all framing members. Patterns simplify making angle cuts. Complete Build It Yourself Pattern Available.

#760 Add-a-Room. Directions simplify building a 12 x 16 and 16 x 24 addition with a shed or gable roof. Full size patterns insure cutting important parts. Book #609 contains a comparable solution to the same problem.

BEDROOM

LAUNDRY OR GUEST ROOM

BATH

#570 Modernize Your Attic. This pattern explains how to transform an attic into an extra bedroom. Step by step directions cover every step. additional information on the same improvement is offered in Book #665.

KITCHEN CABINETS

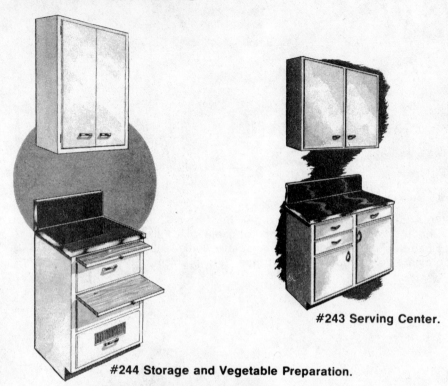

#243 Serving Center.

#244 Storage and Vegetable Preparation.

#41 Sink Enclosure

40

#246 Dish Storage Cabinet,
also in Book #658.

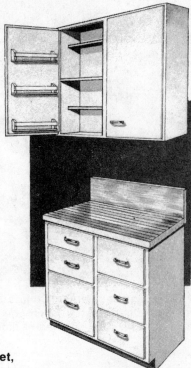

#245 The Mixing Center

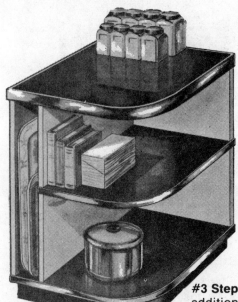

#3 Step-Saver Kitchen Unit. Provides additional table space plus handy storage for toaster, mixer, trays, etc.

#80 Storage and Serving Counter. Complete storage unit contains space for both dining and kitchen equipment. Shelves and drawers can be opened from either kitchen or dining side.

#158 Lavatory Enclosure. Put waste space beneath your lavatory to work with this modern enclosure.

#770 Can Storage on Door. Double kitchen shelf space with this easy to build storage door unit. Can be built to fit any size door, also in Book #634.

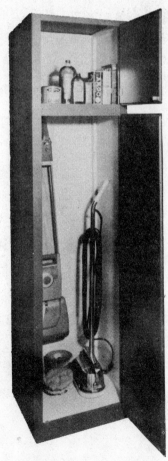

#156 Cleaning Closet. Big cabinet provides ample room for vacuum cleaner, brooms, mops, duster, assortment of cleaners and waxes.

SPORTSMAN'S CABINET — RACKS

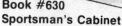

**Book #630
Sportsman's Cabinet**

#266 Sportsman's Cabinet. Hunting and fishing needs can be neatly stowed in this roomy cabinet. One side has space for rods and guns. Cabinet revolves on base for access to opposite side containing hanger space for hunting jacket and sport clothing. Drawers and shelves permit storing ammunition, reels, tackles, boxes, etc., also in Book #630.

44

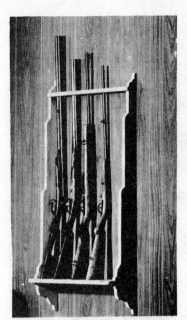

These gun and fishing rod racks can be built by following directions in Book #630.

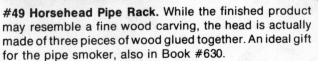

#49 Horsehead Pipe Rack. While the finished product may resemble a fine wood carving, the head is actually made of three pieces of wood glued together. An ideal gift for the pipe smoker, also in Book #630.

RECORD CABINETS

#192 Modern Record Cabinet.
Also in Book #664.

#436 Record Cabinet. These compact well designed cabinets offer ideal space for storage of records and related items.

#191 Castilian Cabinets. Preformed plastic plaques simplify building this Spanish style cabinet.

TV — HI-FI — SEWING • TABLES AND CABINETS

#272 Hi-Fi Cabinet. Build your own matching Hi-Fi, TV and speaker cabinets. Cabinet at right features a pull out turntable drawer and space for tuner and amplifier.

#925 TV Step Table. This step table is just the right height for viewing.

#16 Revolving TV Table. Yours for better viewing of favorite programs.

#543 Sewing Table-Cabinet.

#139 Wardrobe. Sliding doors conceal big closet on one side, five drawers on other.

#265 Cedar Room . Put an unfinished portion of your attic to good use by building a Cedar Room. Clothing, woolens and linens are assured convenient off-season storage. Pattern clearly illustrates the simplest and most economical way to build this room to any size desired. Building details also explained in Book #634.

CHESTS

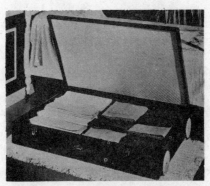

#37 Under Bed Storage Chest.
This big dustproof, space saving
chest provides a wonderful place
to keep linens, blankets. Also in
Book #634.

#962 Blanket Chest. You don't need to
be a skilled craftsman to build this colonial
chest. Carved wood trim available in lumber
yards adds professional finish. Construction
details also provided in Book #761.

BEDS

#68 Single or Double Bed. A replica of the under-the-eaves bed used in Colonial times. Pattern provides instructions for making a single or double size bed, also in Book #761. A miniature bed for the doll house set is shown in Book #753.

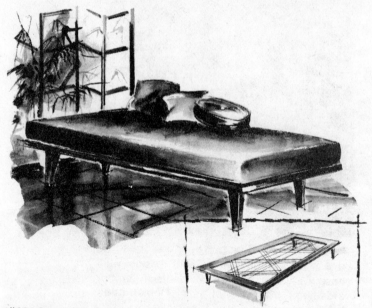

#633 Studio Bed. Only stock lumber and nylon cord required to build the frame and legs of this handsome studio bed. Also in Book #623.

#87 Bunk Beds.

#773 Colonial Baby Cradle. Also in Book #761. A miniature cradle is shown in Book #753.

HEADBOARD STORAGE UNITS

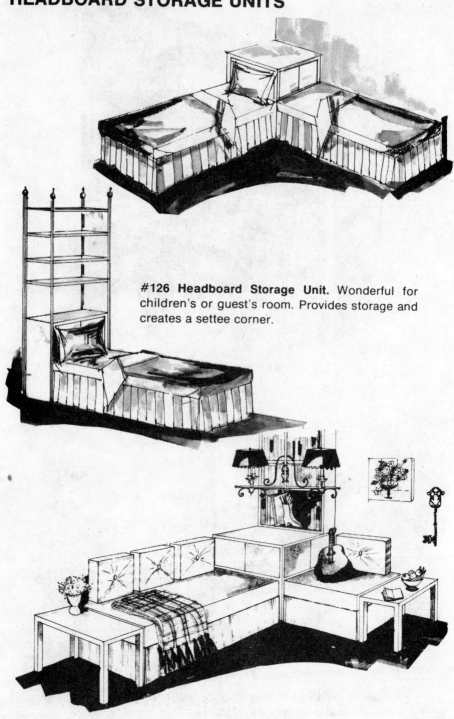

#126 Headboard Storage Unit. Wonderful for children's or guest's room. Provides storage and creates a settee corner.

DIVIDERS

#128 Room Divider. Place one over one and you create an excellent grill for screening dining area. Also in Book #664.

Construction of these room dividers is detailed in Book #658.

DESKS — BOOKCASES

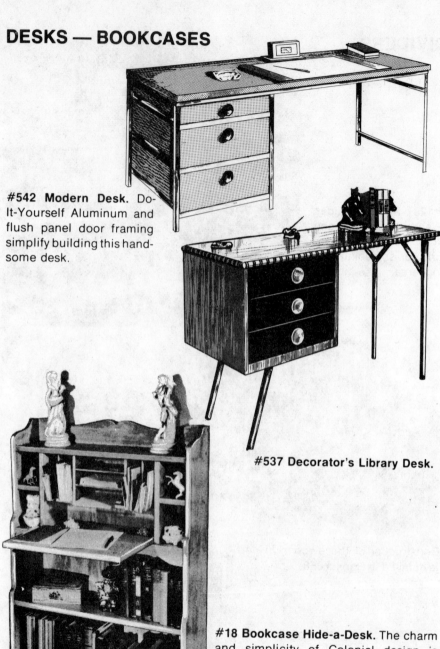

#542 Modern Desk. Do-It-Yourself Aluminum and flush panel door framing simplify building this handsome desk.

#537 Decorator's Library Desk.

#18 Bookcase Hide-a-Desk. The charm and simplicity of Colonial design is emphasized in this 45 x 29'' combination bookcase. Construction detail is also provided in Book #761. A miniature is shown in Book #753.

#719 Bookcase. Wall to wall bookcase provides both drawer and cabinet space. Pattern explains how to build case to fit any available space. Easy to install plastic drawers, specified in list of materials, simplify building. Also in Book #664.

Modern Four Piece Bookcase Ensemble. These are ideally suited for use in any room. Patterns provide complete information for building to length required. Construction details are included in Book #664.

#555 Artist's Easel. Light and durable, easel adjusts to any height desired, and folds compactly.

ASSORTED BARS

#327 Bathtub Beauty Bar.

#718 Buffet Bar.

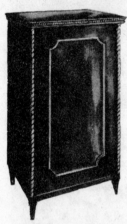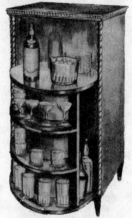

#508 Cabinet Bar. Also in Book #690.

A*

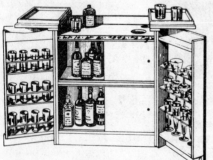

A*

A*

COLONIAL TAVERN BAR CABINET. Measuring 43" wide, 14" deep, 82" high, this handsome two part highboy contains a wall cabinet with storage doors, a mobile bar that can be moved into position wherever required. Book #612.

Order full size patterns by number indicated. Book #690 explains construction of AB.

B*

BARS • TABLES

C*

D*

Night Table with drawers in the Spanish Period, Book #608.

E*

Order full size patterns by number indicated. Book #690 contains directions for building CDE.

#774 Console Table. Thanks to marble-ized Con-Tact, these tables are easy to build. Pattern provides complete directions for building a console or hall table, round, square or rectangular coffee tables. New Danish table bracket, plastic and brass legs so simplify building, table can be made in an evening's time.

#309 Modern Coffee Table.
Smart and modern, the top of this table offers ample space for the various uses you will want to put it to.

#52 Salisbury Coffee Table.
This combination serving tray and stand make an ideal coffee table. Stand folds when not in use.

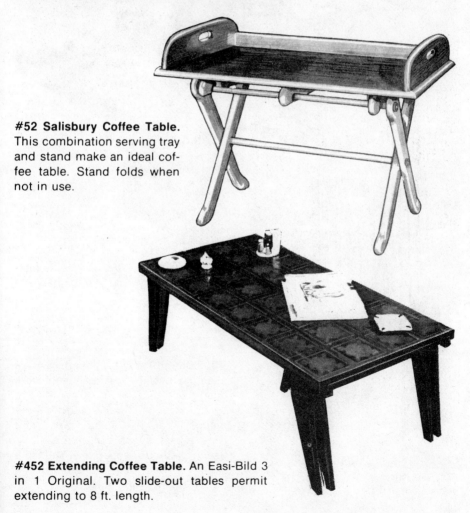

#452 Extending Coffee Table. An Easi-Bild 3 in 1 Original. Two slide-out tables permit extending to 8 ft. length.

TABLES • BUFFET

#140 Sliding Top Coffee Table. The top of this table slides back to reveal ample room for glassware, magazines, checkers or chess. Bottles can be stored in hollow legs.

#137 Dining Table. This handsome table was built from plywood and lumber.

#308 Dining Table & Cabinet. Here's a specially designed combination room divider and dinette. This attractive and serviceable unit consists of three pieces; Storage Cabinet, Grille and Dining Table. Each can be made and used together or separately. The table seats five comfortably. A planter can be built in top of cabinet if desired.

#17 Peasant Table. Make a table and bench set for dining room or kitchen. Also suitable for porch or lawn.

#43 Folding Snack Tables. Ideal for informal dining or television "snack" time.

#138 Dining Buffet. Two spacious drawers above, storage space on shelves below make this buffet a stunning addition to dining room.

61

TABLES • CHAIRS

#95 Modern Table. Build one or more to suit your needs.

#306 Modern String Chair. Made of a 2 x 6 piece of lumber and ordinary wrapping cord.

#127 Step End Table. The simple lines of this Step End Table permit using it with almost every style of furniture. Its size makes it ideally suited for use at the end of a couch, armchair or as an individual piece in the living or bedroom. A perfect companion piece to the furniture built from Patterns #126, 128, 129.

#92 Modern Chair. Build this chair with or without arms.

#141 Cabinet End Table. Place at end of couch or chair.

#99 Modern End Table is easy to build. No special tools or skill required.

DINING BENCH • RACKS

#307 Dining Bench. While designed for use with Dinette Pattern #308, this bench will be welcome and in demand in every home that carries a television aerial. Handy, spacious, comfortable and modern, it will blend in with you other furnishings.

#920 Magazine & Book Rack. A magazine rack of unusual design.

#345 Shoe Rack.

COLONIAL FURNITURE

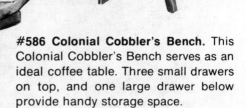

#586 Colonial Cobbler's Bench. This Colonial Cobbler's Bench serves as an ideal coffee table. Three small drawers on top, and one large drawer below provide handy storage space.

Order full size patterns by number indicated. Book #761 also explains building all these pieces.

#270 Hutch Cabinet.

#38 Corner Cabinet.

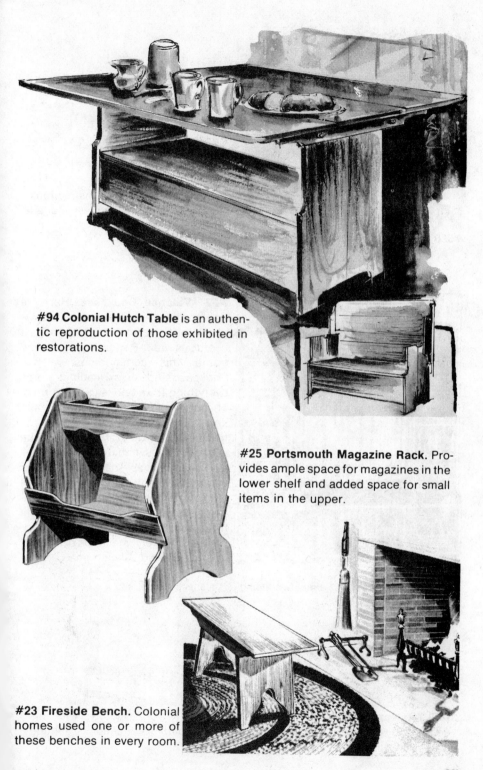

#94 Colonial Hutch Table is an authentic reproduction of those exhibited in restorations.

#25 Portsmouth Magazine Rack. Provides ample space for magazines in the lower shelf and added space for small items in the upper.

#23 Fireside Bench. Colonial homes used one or more of these benches in every room.

65

VALANCES *

#550 Decorator's Valance.

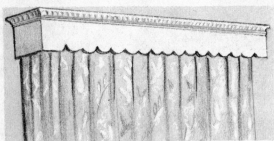

#27 Window Valance. Complete instructions for fitting valance to any size window included with the pattern.

#271 Valance Bookcase. Here's a way to give your favorite window a glamorous treatment and make it useful as well. Perfect as a window frame, this commodious valance bookcase and record cabinet stores everything from books to bric-a-brac. The modern cabinets with their ample and varied storage space can be made to fit the width of your favorite window. The symmetrical bookcases also stand in as shadow boxes for ceramics, plants and other art objects. Connect these with the decorative board across the top, and you will have a window frame deluxe. Directions also cover installation of indirect lighting behind valance board.

*Directions in Book #627 simplify building all valances except #271.

#30 Mt. Vernon Window Valance. Add charm to your windows with this decorative valance. Easy to make and to hang. Complete directions for fitting to all size windows included.

#157 Indirect Lighting Valance. The extra depth of this decorative valance allows room for curtain rods and fluorescent light units. Pattern adjusts to fit any size window. At night, the concealed lighting will bathe an entire room with a soft glow. It's easy and inexpensive to build it yourself.

#159M Collector's Display Case.

#1 Wide Window Valance and Side Shelves.

#159 Frame A Window or a Wall with this easy to follow pattern.

KITCHEN RACKS ● SHELVES

#2 Peasant Shelf. You can make this shelf in an evening's time. No special tools or skill required. Trace pattern on wood, saw and assemble exactly as step by step directions indicate. Full size painting guides assure decorating with a professional touch.

#8 Knife and Implement Rack. Do you have difficulty locating the right ladle, knife, bottle or can opener when you need them? This implement rack will save time and temper. It provides a handy place to keep your sharpest knives and other constantly needed gadgets ready for instant use.

#4 Narrow Peasant Shelf. Full size decorating guides for floral design assure professional results.

#578 Cabinet Message Center. This ingenious little cupboard provides the answer to many of kitchen storage problems. The lower door acts as a blackboard on which you can write your grocery lists or messages.

#5 Decorator's Kitchen Shelf. Hard-to-find kitchen gadgets will always be within easy reach if you keep them on this kitchen shelf.

SHELVES

#21 Hanging Bookshelf. Perfect for books, bric-a-brac, radio, clock, spice boxes, etc.

#31 New Castle Whatnot Shelf. This charming Colonial shelf provides an ideal place to display miniatures, china and other small objects. Whether painted or stained these shelves add a decorator's touch.

#6 All-Purpose Shelf.

#313 Telephone Shelf. Built-in blackboard eliminates lost messages.

#24 Maryland Wall Shelf. Display china, glassware, silverware, etc., on this charming shelf.

71

SHELVES

#35 Duncan Knicknack Shelf. Pattern provides complete directions for making either a corner or wall shelf. Directions are also included in Book #756.

#82 Modern Planter. A practical and attractive solution to the problem of keeping potted plants indoors.

#7 Flower Pot Holder. This decorative flower pot holder will add a note of color to your window. Potted plants thrive on its light and airy shelves. To capture the maximum amount of sunshine, the shelves can be raised, lowered or turned as needed. Directions for fitting to any size window are included on pattern.

#46 Circus Wagon Plant Holder. This gaily decorated miniature circus wagon makes a colorful flowerpot holder.

#933 Colonial Planter. These add a charming note. Pattern provides complete directions for building three different styles.
Patterns for building Colonial Planters are also included in Book #761.

WALL ORNAMENTS

#301 Shadow Boxes. Full size patterns simplify making these decorative Shadow Boxes.

#559 Candle Wall Sconce. A delightfully different wall decoration.

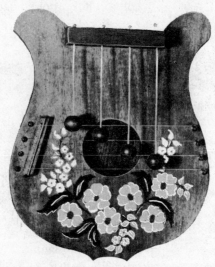

#561 Swedish Door Chimes. Hang these decorative door chimes on the inside of your front door and visitors will be welcomed with a musical greeting. Directions also in Book #677.

74

#580 FLYING GEESE

#581 ROOSTER

#539 PRIMITIVE

Decorate your family room with these easy to make wall plaques.

Aluminum sheet, scissors, plus full size patterns simplify tracing and cutting plaques to exact shape shown. Finish with decorator color desired.

LAMPS AND LIGHTING

#98 Modern Lamps. These lamps are easy and inexpensive to make. Simplified instructions take all the mystery out of wiring.

#533 Rooster Pin-Up Lamp. You don't need to be an expert to make this decorative pin-up lamp.

#541 Planter Lamp. Full size patterns simplify making and decorating this handsome Planter Lamp and Shade.

76

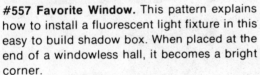

#557 Favorite Window. This pattern explains how to install a fluorescent light fixture in this easy to build shadow box. When placed at the end of a windowless hall, it becomes a bright corner.

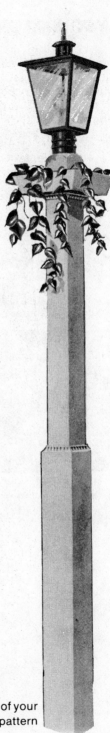

#935 Colonial Lamp Post. Enhance the driveway of your home with this easy to build lamp post. Full size pattern also in Book #607.

PLYSCULPTURE

No special skill or artistic ability is needed to transform plywood into magnificent murals. Full Size Plysculpture Patterns provide a quick, easy and accurate way of adding a custom-made look to furniture, walls and flush panel doors.

#712 Oriental Folding Screen.
#706 Blue Willow Screen.

#713 Kitchen Decoration.

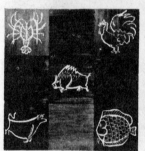

#705 Tile-A-Wall Plaques.

#702 Waterfront Scene

#709 Egyptian Design. #701 Tree of Life Design.#704 Oriental Door Panel.

HOME IMPROVEMENTS

#231 Fireplace Mantel. Four concealed, hinged panels open to permit using this mantel on a prefabricated fireplace. Whether you build a mantel, garage, kitchen cabinets or any home improvement, you not only save money but also have the opportunity of enjoying many relaxing hours. Working with your hands provides release from nervous tension, escape from everyday problems while it transforms spare time into sizable savings. Directions for building mantel also included in Books #605 and 674.

WORKBENCHES • TOOLCHEST

#568 Store-All Workbench. Through an ingenious, yet simple, method of construction, this workbench provides two 6 ft. vises and two big perforated hardboard tool compartments at each end.

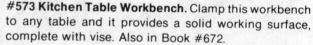

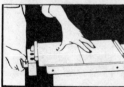

CLAMP FOR PLANING

#573 Kitchen Table Workbench. Clamp this workbench to any table and it provides a solid working surface, complete with vise. Also in Book #672.

GLUE BOARDS TOGETHER

#45 Sawhorse Shoeshine Box.

VISE FOR SAWING

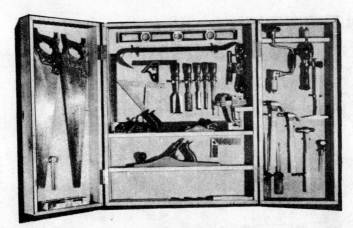

#71 Tool Chest. Hang it on the wall or fold it up. Large enough to hold a really workable assortment of tools. Also in Book #634.

CIGARETTE AND MATCH CRADLE

FERN SCROLL SHELF

COBBLER'S BENCH SEWING KIT

COLONIAL PLANTER

WADDLING WILLIE PULL TOY

PONY BOOK ENDS

MARY AND LAMB WALL PLAQUE

Full size patterns also in Book #756.

STRING HOLDER

#102A Jig Saw Pattern Assortment. There's fun and fascination for all from seven to seventy. Projects are simple, easy to build and easy to decorate by following full size painting guides. All are interesting, well styled articles, ideally suited for gifts or for starting a part or full time business.

LAWN FURNITURE

#32/39 Briarcliff Lawn Chair and Lawn Settee. Curved seat and back make this chair truly comfortable. Handsome settee matches chair. Step by step construction details are also included in Book #754.

#322R Sectional Lawn Chair. Group two or more of these chairs together to form a sectional settee. Arms can be built on either or both sides.

#311 Modern Lawn Chair. This taped chair makes a handsome addition to a terrace, porch or lawn.

#169 Lawn Chair. Chaise and Settee.

#132 Child Size Lawn Chair. A junior size to match chair made from #32. Both patterns included in Book #754.

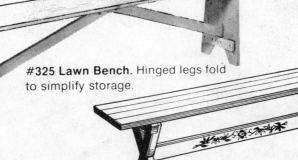

#325 Lawn Bench. Hinged legs fold to simplify storage.

#57 Peasant Bench. An ideal bench for use on porch or lawn. Full size patterns permit tracing decoration.

83

CHAIRS • CHAISES • TABLE

#55/56 Foldaway Garden Chair and Settee. Form fitting chair and settee fold for easy storage.

#312 Beverly Hills Chaise. Adjustable back rest on this chaise offers the ultimate in comfort. Construction also included in Book #754.

#75 Terrace Table. Use with or without large umbrella.

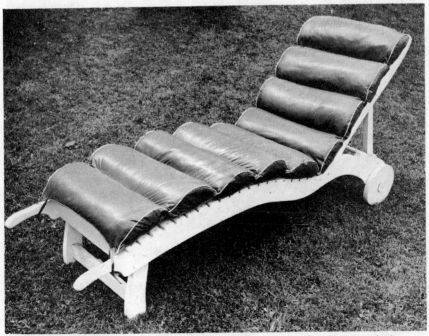

#78 Garden Chaise. Relax in sun or shade on this handsome chaise.

PICNIC TABLES • CHAIR

#326 Terrace or Coffee Table. Table can easily be taken apart for off season storage. Construction also explained in Book #754.

#554 Outdoor Dining Table. This handsome table provides the center of attraction at every outdoor gathering.

#548 Modern Web Chair. Wood, aluminum and plastic webbing simplify building this chair.

#577 Lifetime Picnic Table. Easy-to-build picnic table is constructed on steel, wood or concrete posts.

#323 6 ft. Picnic Table. A must for out-of-doors dining. Top folds over, seats swing up when table is not in use. Construction also explained in Book #754.

PICNIC TABLE • PORCH

#22 Picnic Table and Benches. This 6 ft. table is a must for picnics out of doors. Its construction permits easy storing when not in use.

#567 Add-A-Porch. This pattern simplifies building a porch to almost any size and height required. Construction also explained in Book #63l.

CARPORT

#273 Town and Country Carport. Can be easily built onto your house or garage and modified to serve as a porch or patio. Construction also included in Book #680.

GARAGE • GARAGE DOOR • SHED

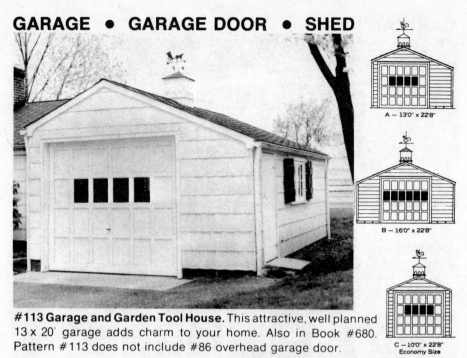

A — 13'0" x 22'8"

B — 16'0" x 22'8"

C — 10'0" x 22'8"
Economy Size

#113 Garage and Garden Tool House. This attractive, well planned 13 x 20' garage adds charm to your home. Also in Book #680. Pattern #113 does not include #86 overhead garage door.

#86 Automatic Swing-Up Garage Door. Pattern simplifies building swing-up type of door for single, as well as a two car door up to 16 ft. wide. Construction also explained in Book #763.

#89 Lean-To Shed. No special skill or experience needed to add this handy storage shed to side of house or garage. Construction also explained in Book #649.

BAR-B-QUE • FIREPLACE

#316 Superchef Barbecue. Picnics in your own backyard are fun when meals are cooked on this man-sized barbecue. Step by step construction also offered in Book #668.

Outdoor Fireplace. Easi-Bild method takes mystery out of building. Book #668.

CONCRETE PROJECTS

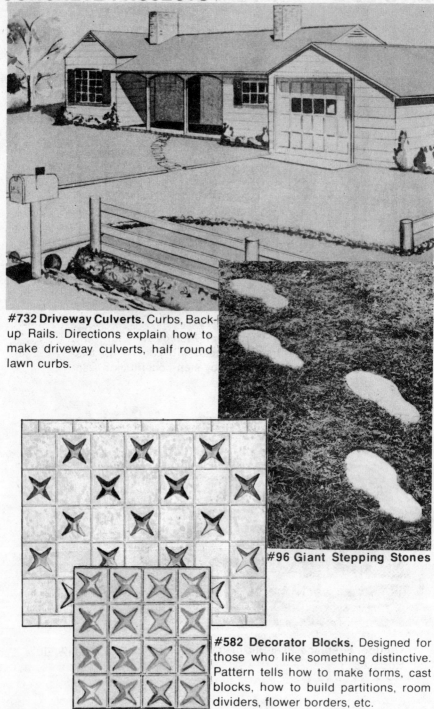

#732 Driveway Culverts. Curbs, Back-up Rails. Directions explain how to make driveway culverts, half round lawn curbs.

#96 Giant Stepping Stones

#582 Decorator Blocks. Designed for those who like something distinctive. Pattern tells how to make forms, cast blocks, how to build partitions, room dividers, flower borders, etc.

PATIO

#591 Pave-A-Patio. No special skill or masonry experience is needed to pave an outdoor living room. Directions also in Book #606 and #617.

FENCES • DOOR CANOPY

#315 Williamsburg Fence and Gate.
Build authentic Williamsburg picket fence
and matching gate at a fraction of retail
cost.

#305 Door Canopy. Shelter
entrance to your home with
this canopy.

#937 Garden Privacy Partition. Ingenious design permits a free flow
of summer breezes. Also in Book #631.

Order full size pattern by number indicated. Book #607 explains all
projects except #937.

GATES

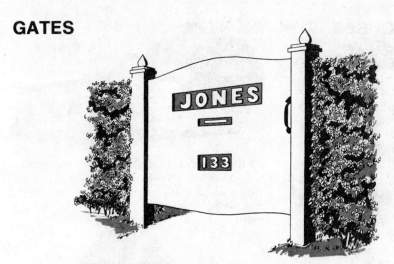

#934 Nameplate Gate. Identify your property with this unique gate.

#941 Rail Fence and Gate. Beautify your property with this Rail Fence and Gate.

BIRDHOUSES

#9 Bird Feeder. This cleverly designed combination Weathervane and Feeding Station indicates direction of wind while providing complete protection for your feathered friends.

#11 Wren House. This attractive slatted roof Wren House is an easy one to build. Just trace, saw and assemble exactly as instructions indicate.

#111 Wren House. Building birdhouses can be lots of fun. They are easy to make and offer much in return. In song and in the destruction of harmful insects, you are repaid many times for the effort expended.

#110 Bluebird House. The bluebird has always been considered a harbinger of good luck - so welcome him with this delightful home.

#10 Birdhouse. Bird watching can provide many pleasant moments of complete relaxation for those who provide shelter for our feathered friends. Full size painting guides simplify decorating.

Construction of #9, 11, 110, 111 also included in Book #669.

ANIMAL SHELTERS

#724 Cat Shelter. Allows pets complete freedom. Pattern simplifies building and installing in basement or first floor window.

#28 All Weather Dog House. Affords real protection in all kinds of weather. Inner partition and removable end permits use all year.

Order full size pattern by number indicated. Book #751 also explains building these shelters.

ANIMAL SHELTERS

#725 Duck Inn. Complete with swimming pool and private entrance. Full size pattern also in Book #751.

#13 All Weather Hog House. Leading agricultural experts recommend this hog house. Hinged roof permits safe inspection of sows.

#14 Westchester Poultry House. Construction of this 10 ft. house has been so simplified a schoolboy can build it.

DOUBLE DUTY WINDOW PROJECTS

#135 Home Air Cooler. Build a breeze. Lower indoor temperature as much as 10 degrees. Simplified directions take mystery out of building.

#303 Storm Windows. Cut winter fuel bills by installing storm windows.

#566 Window Greenhouse. Everyone who likes plants will be intrigued with this low cost greenhouse. Full size pattern also in Book #611.

WEATHERVANES • SCREEN

#588 Sailor Weathervane. Determine
the winds on a nautical basis with this
sailor weathervane.

#524 Rooster Weather Vane. Place
this proud rooster on house or
garage and he'll tell which say the
wind blows.

#930 Room Screen. This unique folding screen
complements the furnishings of almost any
room.

LAWN ACCESSORIES

#801 - 7" Display Letters.

#438 Drive Slow Safety Sign. 55" policeman is a worthwhile project. Place one next to your driveway.

#93 Bulletin Board. Every doctor, lawyer, church, store or school can use this locktype Bulletin Board. Directions for building also offered in Book #607.

#81 Lawn Ornaments. Add a rural touch to your front lawn. Patterns are also provided in Book #672.

PLAYGROUND EQUIPMENT

#733 Merry-Go-Round. This easy to build merry-go-round will create many happy childhood memories. Full size pattern simplifies making and decorating swan, giraffe, pony and jet plane.

#40 Rocket Express Wagon. This 32" Express Wagon can be made from short lengths of lumber.

#20 Happy Hour Sandbox. The answer to your child's playtime hours. Full size decorating guides included.

102

#63 Child's Slide. Solve your child's playtime hours by making one of these colorful slides.

#153 Jungle Gym. Children love climbing these bars. They spend countless hours building sturdy bodies.

#152 Complete Gymnasium. Two swings, seesaw, climbing rope and horizontal bar provide countless hours of healthy playtime.

#154 Climbing Pole. Here's one of the most popular pieces of playground equipment.

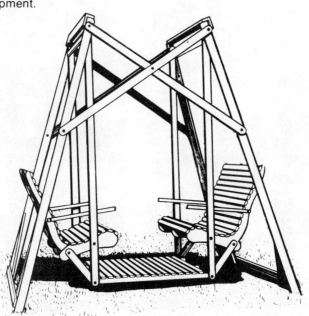

#155 Lawn Glider. Brings back memories of childhood summer evenings. This modern version of an old fashioned lawn swing helps develop many happy moments. Also in Book #754.

PLAYROOM FURNITURE

#65 Toy Chest on Wheels. Children's blocks, soldiers and other toys can be stored in this big chest.

#353 Tot's Step Stool and TV Chair. This versatile step stool raises small fry to the right height for bathroom washups.

#34 Joe Giraffe Clothes Tree. This colorful character provides a place for child's clothing, shoes, etc.

#53 Pony Ride Rocker.

#117 Child's Blackboard Playtable. With top up, it's a blackboard; with top down, it's a dandy playtable.

TOYS

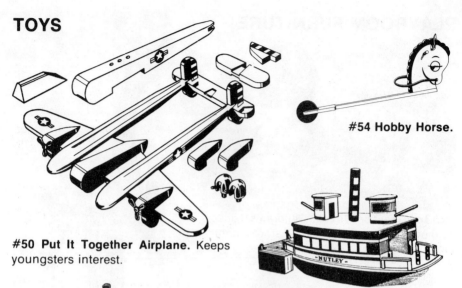

#50 Put It Together Airplane. Keeps youngsters interest.

#54 Hobby Horse.

#67 Come-Apart Ferry Boat is an instructive toy.

#552 Ski-Hi Stilts. Your youngsters will get a kick out of strutting around on these adjustable stilts.

#66 Wheelbarrow. Boys like this big sturdily built 46'' wheelbarrow. Sides are removable.

106

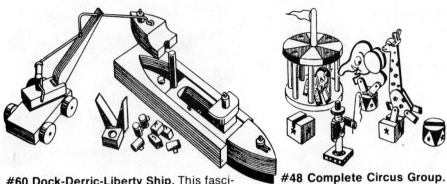

#60 Dock-Derric-Liberty Ship. This fascinating come-apart, put-it-together toy is really tops.

#48 Complete Circus Group.

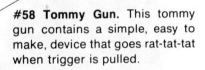

#58 Tommy Gun. This tommy gun contains a simple, easy to make, device that goes rat-tat-tat when trigger is pulled.

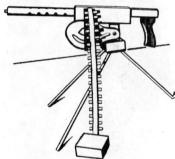

#70 Cargo Glider with Jeep and Tank. Front doors on this glider swing open to permit loading a tank and jeep.

#62 Machine Gun. Boys mow 'em down when they turn the crank on this automatic gun.

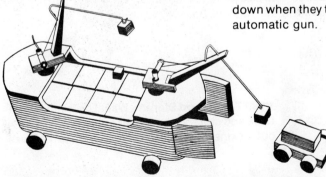

#72 Amphibious Freighter. Many happy playtime hours will be spent piloting this freighter to all parts of the house.

107

Dream Doll House. You can build this house with a hammer, saw and sharp knife, directions in Book #753.

#314 Bermuda Kite. Here's a big, high flying design that's famous for breaking altitude records.

#61 Doll Size Carriage. Full size pattern simplifies building a carriage for a doll, also in Book #753.

#190 Trainboard Storage Wall. This electric train table and storage cabinet takes the fuss and muss out of one of America's most popular hobbies.

#59 Doll Carriage. This big doll carriage is fashioned after those used in Colonial times.

#148 Playhouse-Playstore. Children love to play store and will spend many happy hours playing in this delightful little house. Playhouse measures 4 ft. by 3 ft. 8 inches by 5 ft. 6 inches high and will easily fit in the corner of a room.

SPORTS EQUIPMENT

#161 Relax-A-Board. Spend ten to fifteen minutes a day on this board and you'll be amazed at the relaxing results.

#594 Portable Pick-Up Truck. Anyone who wants to get away for an inexpensive vacation can save money staying overnight in this easy to build bunkhouse.

#583 Cari-Car. Pattern provides complete, easy to follow directions for assembling this handy, gas powered buggy. Ideal for golf course. Perfect for the young as well as aged and infirm.

BOATS

#248 Sail Scooter. Only a light breeze is required and "away you'll go." It offers real sailing fun at lowest possible cost.

#194 Seabreeze Sailboat. Another Easi-Bild Original. Full Size Frame Patterns plus easy to follow directions simplify building this 12 ft. centerboard sailboat.

#85 - 11½ Ft. General Utility Boat. Sturdy construction permits using 2 h.p. to 10 h.p. outboard motor. Yet it's light enough to handle easily with a pair of oars.

111

#317 Kayak. For Sportsmen only. Light and fast, it takes skill and practice to handle. Full size patterns take mystery out of building.

#247 Cartop Swimming Float. This easy-to-build 10 ft. surfboard or swimming float is at home in rough water or a quiet pond.

#77 Sportsman's Barge-Boat. Flat-bottomed scow is easy to build and fun to use. Ideal for duck shooting or fishing near shore. Youngsters can use it on pond, lake or stream.

112

BUILD A HOUSEBOAT TO HAPPINESS #676-26

No special skill or experience is required. Much preliminary work can be done, prior to final assembly, in basement-workshop or garage. The spare time you invest can equal more than half the cost of any comparable factory-built boat!

#676-26 — 26 ft. x 8 ft. beam. Sleeps four. Can be trailed over the road without permit. Cruise at 8 to 10 m.p.h. with 40 h.p. outboard.

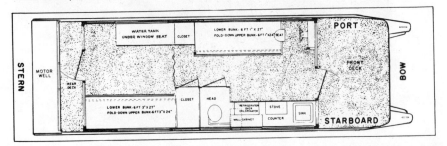

CHRISTMAS DECORATIONS

#431 Santa stands 40''. Place him outdoors on lawn, next to chimney or on top of roof and he'll greet all who pass.

#575 Life Size Santa Claus. This decoration measures 6 ft. high. Dummy packages, stacked on a shelf on back, give the impression Santa is loaded.

#410C Camels.

#433   #434

#433 Reindeer. Make one or a dozen. Adjustable legs add a feeling of animation.

#434 Santa Claus Sleigh. Decorate your lawn, porch or roof with Santa's own Sleigh and Reindeer.

#670 Angel Banner. Colored felt, glue and glitter simplify making a magical Christmas banner.

115

#767 Madonna Christmas Wreath. Full size painting guides simplify painting Madonna and Child with professional results assured.

#435 Colossal Candy Cane. Welcome Christmas callers with this festive 6 ft. Candy Cane.

#531 Noel Christmas Greeting. This lawn, porch or roof decoration extends a colorful greeting to all who pass by day or night.

#942B Christmas Mural Door Panel. The full size pattern provides numbered guides that insure painting scene as illustrated.

116

#942A Christmas Mural Picture Window. Professional results are achieved when you follow the full
size pattern 4 ft. by 6 ft.

#310 Nativity Scene. Patterns make it easy to build
and decorate this colorful replica of the Nativity
Scene.

#410 Life Size Nativity Scene. For those who want
the ultimate in Christmas decorations, this 12 ft.
wide by 8 ft. tall Life Size Nativity Scene is ideally
suited as a church, school or community project.

117

#149 Christmas Window.

#331 Outdoor Christmas Greeting. Throw a spotlight on these 40" high cheerful carolers and they will happily extend Christmas Greetings to all who pass by day or night.

#562 Choir Boys Christmas Greeting. Christmas lights, wired into the 1" pipe "candles" and behind choir boys, provide an entrancing lighting effect after dark.

118

#560 Three Wisemen Greeting. The Three Wisemen approaching the Holy City are portrayed with great dignity and charm in this illuminated "Outdoor Christmas Card."

#769 Christmas Angel.

#540 Outdoor Christmas Card.

#592 4 ft. high Christmas Card.

#768 **Christmas Fireplace.** This 4 ft. wide easy-to-build fireplace mantel makes an ideal Christmas decoration.

Easi-Bild®   LIBRARY BOUND BOOK ORDER FORM

PLEASE SEND THE FOLLOWING:

_____ L03   How to Build a Dormer
_____ L05   How to Panel with Plywood
_____ L06   How to Lay Ceramic Tile
_____ L07   How to Build Outdoor Projects
_____ L08   How to Modernize a Kitchen
_____ L09   How to Build an Addition
_____ L11   How to Build a Walk-In or Window Greenhouse
             Electric Light Gardening Simplified
_____ L120 Stereo Installation Simplified,
             How to Build Wall-to-Wall Cabinets
_____ L13   How to Build or Enclose a Porch
_____ L15   How to Modernize a Basement
_____ L17   Concrete Work Simplified
_____ L23   How to Repair, Refinish & Reupholster Furniture
_____ L27   How to Make Cornice Boards, Draperies, Valances,
             Install Traverse Track
_____ L300 How to Build Sportsman's Revolving Storage Cabinet
_____ L31   How to Build Patios & Sundecks
_____ L32   How to Build a Vacation or Retirement House
_____ L34   How to Build Storage Units
_____ L49   How to Build a Garden Tool House, Child's Playhouse
_____ L58   How to Build Kitchen Cabinets,
             Room Dividers and Cabinet Furniture
_____ L63   How to Build a Two Car Garage
_____ L64   How to Construct Built-In and Sectional Bookcases
_____ L65   How to Modernize an Attic
_____ L68   Bricklaying Simplified
_____ L69   How to Build Birdhouses & Bird Feeders
_____ L72   How to Build Workbenches, Sawhorse Tool Chest
_____ L74   How to Install a Fireplace
_____ L750 Plumbing Repairs Simplified
_____ L77   How to Plan & Build a Home Workshop
_____ L79   How to Build a Stable & Red Barn Tool House
_____ L800 How to Build a One Car Garage, Carport,
             Convert a Garage to a Stable
_____ L82   How to Add an Extra Bathroom
_____ L83   Carpeting Simplified
_____ L84   How to Transform a Garage into Living Space
_____ L85   How to Rehabilitate Abandoned Buildings
_____ L90   How to Build Bars
_____ L94   Easi-Bild Simplifies Electrical Repairs
_____ L95   How to Install Protective Alarm Devices
_____ L96   Roofing Simplified
_____ L97   Forms, Footings, Foundations, Framing
_____ L51   How to Build Pet Housing
_____ L53   How to Build Dollhouses — Furniture
_____ L54   How to Build Outdoor Furniture
_____ L56   Scroll Saw Projects
_____ L61   How to Build Colonial Furniture

PRICES SUBJECT TO CHANGE WITHOUT NOTICE

121

Easi-Bild® PATTERN ORDER FORM

No. 1 Window Valance	No. 92 Modern Chair
No. 2 Peasant Shelf	No 93 Bulletin Board
No. 3 Kitchen Unit	No. 94 Colonial Hutch Table
No. 4 Narrow Peasant Shelf	No. 95 Modern Table
No. 5 Kitchen Shelf	No. 96 Giant Footprints
No. 6 All Purpose Shelf	No 98 Modern Lamp
No. 7 Flower Pot Holder	No. 99 Modern End Table
No. 8 Knife and Imp. Rack	No. 102A Jig Saw Pattern Asst.
No. 9 Bird Feeder	No. 103H Hillside House Plan
No. 10 Bird House	No. 103V Valley House Plan
No. 11 Wren House	No. 110 Bluebird House
No. 13 Hog House	No. 111 Wren House
No. 14 Poultry House	No. 113 Garage & Tool House
No. 16 Revolving TV Table	No. 117 Child's Playtable
No. 17 Peasant Table	No. 126 Headboard Storage Unit
No. 18 Bookcase Hide-A-Desk	No. 127 Step End Table
No. 20 Sandbox	No. 128 20″ 40″ 80″ Rm.Dividers
No. 21 Hanging Bookshelf	No. 132 Junior Briarcliff Chair
No. 22 Picnic Table	No. 135 Home Air Cooler
No. 23 Fireside Bench	No. 137 Dining Table
No. 24 Wall Shelf	No. 138 Dining Buffet
No. 25 Magazine Rack	No. 139 Wardrobe
No. 27 Window Valance	No. 140 Sliding Top Coffee Table
No. 28 Dog House	No. 141 Cabinet End Table
No. 30 Window Valance	No. 148 Playhouse
No. 31 Whatnot Shelf	No. 149 Christmas Window
No. 32 Lawn Chair	No. 152 Complete Outdoor
No. 39 Lawn Settee	Gymnasium
No. 34 Giraffe Clothestree	No. 153 Jungle Gym
No. 35 Knicknack Shelf	No. 154 Climbing Pole
No. 37 Storage Chest	No. 155 Lawn Glider
No. 38 Corner Cabinet	No. 156 Cleaning Utensil Closet
No. 40 Express Wagon	No. 157 Valance Board
No. 41 Undersink Enclosure	No. 158 Lavatory Enclosure
No. 43 Folding Snack Tables	No. 159M Collector s Display
No. 45 Shoeshine Box	Case
No. 46 Plant Holder	No. 159 Frame A Window
No. 48 Complete Circus	No. 161 Relax-A-Board
No. 49 Horsehead Pipe Rack	No. 169 Lawn Chair & Settee
No. 50 Airplane Group	No. 190 Trainboard Storage
No. 52 Coffee Table	Wall
No. 53 Pony Ride Rocker	No 191 Multiple Moderns
No. 54 Hobby Horse	No. 192 Modern Record Cabinet
No. 55 Foldaway Settee	No. 194 12 ft. Sailboat
No. 56 Foldaway Chair	No. 231 Fireplace Mantel
No. 57 Peasant Bench	No. 243 Serving Center
No. 58 Tommy Gun	No. 244 Storage & Vegetable
No. 59 Doll Carriage	Preparation
No. 60 Dock-Derrick-Ship	No. 245 Mixing Center
No. 61 Baby Doll Carriage	No. 246 Dish Storage Cabinet
No. 62 Machine Gun	No. 247 Cartop Swimming Float
No. 63 Child's Slide	No. 248 Sail Scooter
No. 65 Toy Chest	No. 265 Cedar Room
No. 66 46″ Wheelbarrow	No. 266 Sportsman s Cabinet
No. 67 Come-Apart Ferry	No. 270 Hutch Cabinet
No. 68 Single or Double Bed	No. 271 Valance Bookcase
No. 70 Cargo Glider	No. 272 Hi-Fi Cabinet
No. 71 Tool Chest	No. 273 Town & Country
No. 72 Amphibious Freighter	Carport
No. 75 Terrace Table	No. 301 Shadow Boxes
No. 77 Sportsman's Barge-Boat	No. 303 Storm Window
No. 78 Garden Chaise	No. 305 Canopy
No. 80 Service Counter	No. 306 String Chair
No. 81 Lawn Ornaments	No. 307 Dining Bench
No. 82 Modern Indoor Planter	No. 308 Dinette Room Divider
No 84 Guest & Tourist House	No. 309 Coffee Table
No. 85 Utility Boat	No. 310 Table-top Nativity Scene
No. 86 Swing-up Garage Door	No. 311 Modern Chair
No. 87 Bedford Bunk Beds	No. 312 Beverly Hills Chaise
No. 89 Lean-To Tool Shed	No. 313 Telephone Shelf
No. 91 Country Cottage	No. 314 Bermuda Kite

122

_____ No. 315 Williamsburg Fence Gate
_____ No. 316 Superchef Barbecue
_____ No. 317 Sportsman's Kayak
_____ No. 322R Designer Lawn Chair
_____ No. 323 Folding Picnic Table
_____ No. 325 Lawn Bench
_____ No. 326 Terrace or Coffee Table
_____ No. 327 Bathtub Beauty Bar
_____ No. 331 Outdoor Christmas Greeting
_____ No. 345 Shoe Rack
_____ No. 353 Tot's Step-Stool
_____ No. 410 Life Size Nativity Scene
_____ No. 410C Camel
_____ No. 431 Santa Claus Decoration
_____ No. 432 Southwest Corner House
_____ No. 433 Christmas Reindeer
_____ No. 434 Santa Claus Sleigh
_____ No. 435 Colossal Candy Cane
_____ No. 436 Record Cabinet
_____ No. 438 Drive-Slo Safety Sign
_____ No. 452 Extending Coffee Table
_____ No. 501 Three Bedroom House
_____ No. 502 Six Room Modern House
_____ No. 508 Cabinet Bar
_____ No. 513 Three Bdrm. House Plan
_____ No. 514 Cape Cod House
_____ No. 524 Rooster Weathervane
_____ No. 531 Noel Christmas Greeting
_____ No. 533 Rooster Pin-up Lamp
_____ No. 537 Decorator's Library Desk
_____ No. 539 Do-it-Yourself Primitives
_____ No. 540 4 ft. High Madonna Christmas Card
_____ No. 541 Planter Lamp
_____ No. 542 Modern Desk
_____ No. 543 Sewing Table Cabinet
_____ No. 548 Modern Web Chair
_____ No. 550 Decorator's Valance
_____ No. 552 Ski-Hi Stilts
_____ No. 554 Outdoor Dining Table
_____ No. 555 Artist's Easel
_____ No. 557 How to Light a Dark Corner
_____ No. 559 Candle Wall Sconce
_____ No. 560 Three Wisemen Christmas Greeting
_____ No. 561 Swedish Door Chimes
_____ No. 562 Choir Boys Christmas Greeting
_____ No. 566 Window Greenhouse
_____ No. 567 Add-A-Porch
_____ No. 568 Stor-all Workbench
_____ No. 570 Modernize Your Attic
_____ No. 573 Kitchen Table Workbench
_____ No. 575 6 ft. Santa Claus
_____ No. 577 Lifetime Picnic Table
_____ No. 578 Cabinet Message Center
_____ No. 580 Geese Wall Plaques
_____ No. 581 Rooster Wall Plaques
_____ No. 582 Decorator Blocks
_____ No. 583 Cari-Car
_____ No. 586 Colonial Cobbler's Bench
_____ No. 588 Sailor Weathervane
_____ No. 591 Pave-a-Patio

_____ No. 592 Outdoor Christmas Card
_____ No. 594 Pick-up Truck Body
_____ No. 633 Studio Bed
_____ No. 670 Angel Banner
_____ No. 676 26 ft. House Boat
_____ No. 718 Buffet Bar
_____ No. 719 Bookcase
_____ No. 724 Cat Shelter
_____ No. 725 Duck Inn
_____ No. 732 Driveway Culverts & Curbs
_____ No. 733 Merry-Go-Round
_____ No. 760 Add-a-Room
_____ No. 767 Madonna Christmas Wreath
_____ No. 768 Christmas Fireplace
_____ No. 769 Christmas Angel
_____ No. 770 Can Storage
_____ No. 773 Colonial Baby Cradle
_____ No. 774 Console Table
_____ No. 801 Display Letters
_____ No. 910 Two Bedroom House
_____ No. 920 Magazine & Book Rack
_____ No. 925 TV Step Table
_____ No. 930 Folding Room Screen
_____ No. 933 Three Colonial Planters
_____ No. 934 Name-Plate Gate
_____ No. 935 Colonial Lamp Post
_____ No. 937 Garden Privacy Partition
_____ No. 941 Rail Fence and Gate
_____ No. 942A Paint-It-Yourself Christmas Picture Window 4 ft. x 6 ft.
_____ No. 942B Paint-It-Yourself Christmas Mural Door Size
_____ No. 962 Storage Chest

PLYSCULPTURE PATTERNS

_____ No. 701 Tree of Life Design
_____ No. 702 Waterfront Scene
_____ No. 704 Oriental Door Panel
_____ No. 705 Tile-A-Wall Plaques
_____ No. 706 Blue Willow Screen
_____ No. 709 Egyptian Wall Design
_____ No. 712 Oriental Folding Screen
_____ No. 713 Kitchen Cabinet Decoration

PRICES SUBJECT TO CHANGE WITHOUT NOTICE

123

INDEX TO MONEY-SAVING REPAIRS, IMPROVEMENTS, PATTERNS AND BOOKS
(Number designates EASI-BILD Pattern or Book)

INDEX TO MONEY-SAVING REPAIRS, IMPROVEMENTS, PATTERNS AND BOOKS

126

INDEX TO MONEY-SAVING REPAIRS, IMPROVEMENTS, PATTERNS AND BOOKS